Ludwig van Beethoven

COMPLETE STRING QUARTETS
Transcribed for Four-Hand Piano

Ludwig van Beethoven

COMPLETE STRING QUARTETS
Transcribed for Four-Hand Piano

Transcription by Hugo Ulrich and Robert Wittmann

SERIES I

(Opp. 18 and 59)

Dover Publications, Inc., New York

Published in Canada by General Publishing Company, Ltd., 30 Lesmill Road, Don Mills, Toronto, Ontario.

Published in the United Kingdom by Constable and Company, Ltd., 10 Orange Street, London WC2H 7EG.

This edition, first published in 1980 by Dover Publications, Inc., is an unabridged republication of Opp. 18 and 59, complete, as originally published by C. F. Peters (n.d.). Op. 18 and Op. 59, Nos. 1 and 2 originally appeared within the series *Duos, Trios, Quartette, Quintette, Sextette von L. van Beethoven für Pianoforte zu vier Händen arrangirt von Hugo Ulrich u. Rob. Wittmann*, C. F. Peters, Leipzig, in three volumes with the publication numbers 7768, 7769 and 8001. Op. 59, No. 3 originally appeared within the series *Duos, Trios, Quartette, Quintette, Sextette, Septett und Concerte von L. van Beethoven. Für Pianoforte zu 4 Händen*, C. F. Peters, Bureau de Musique, Leipzig & Berlin, in a volume bearing publication number 5407.

The publisher is grateful to the Queens College Library for making the original editions available for reproduction.

International Standard Book Number: 0-486-23974-8
Library of Congress Catalog Card Number: 80-65317

Manufactured in the United States of America
Dover Publications, Inc.
180 Varick Street
New York, N.Y. 10014

CONTENTS

Ludwig van Beethoven

COMPLETE STRING QUARTETS

Transcribed for Four-Hand Piano

No. 1 in F Major, Op. 18, No. 1

No. 1 in F Major, Op. 18, No. 1

Adagio affettuoso ed appassionato.

Adagio affettuoso ed appassionato.

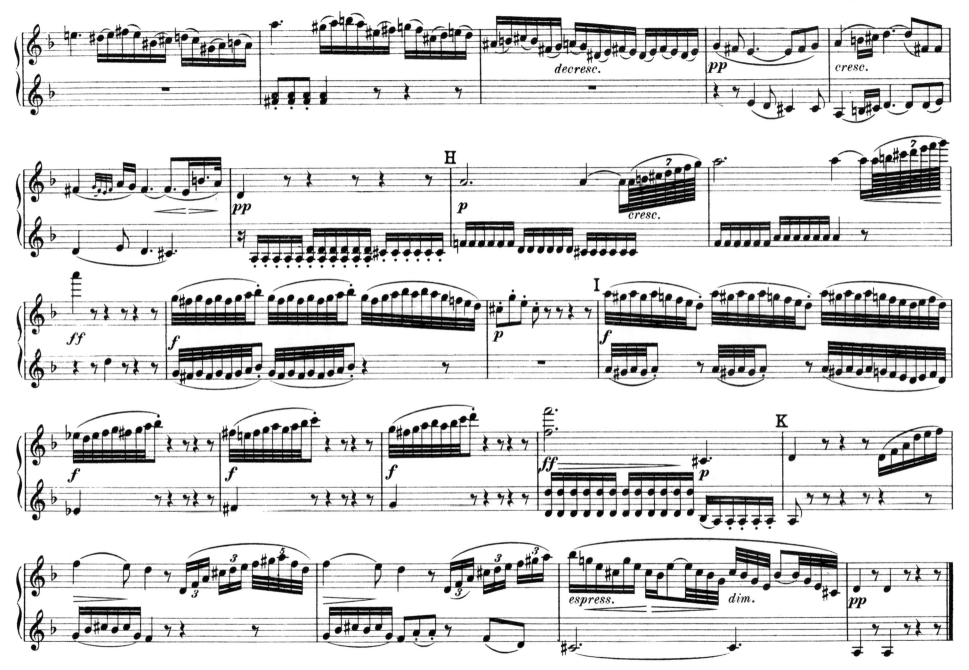

Scherzo.
Allegro molto.

Scherzo.
Allegro molto.

Trio.

Scherzo D. C.

Allegro.

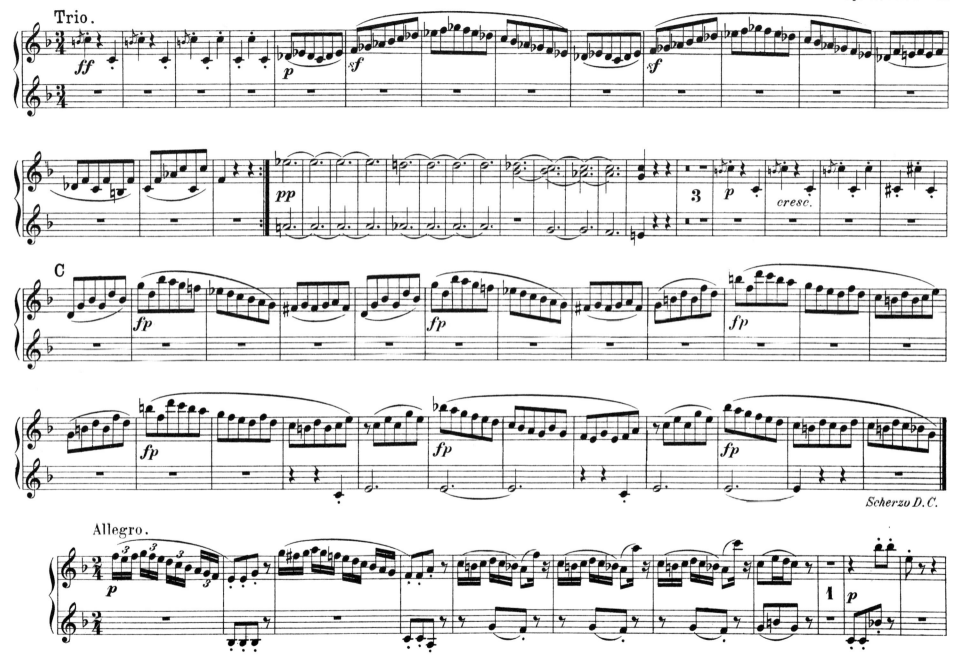

Scherzo D.C.

No. 2 in G Major, Op. 18, No. 2

Allegro.

Secondo.

No. 2 in G Major, Op. 18, No. 2

pp
pp
cresc.
f
3
3
F
p
sf p
sf
p
sf p
sf p
decresc.
p
G
sf
dolce
cresc.
f
p
1

Adagio cantabile.

Adagio cantabile.

Allegro.

Tempo primo.

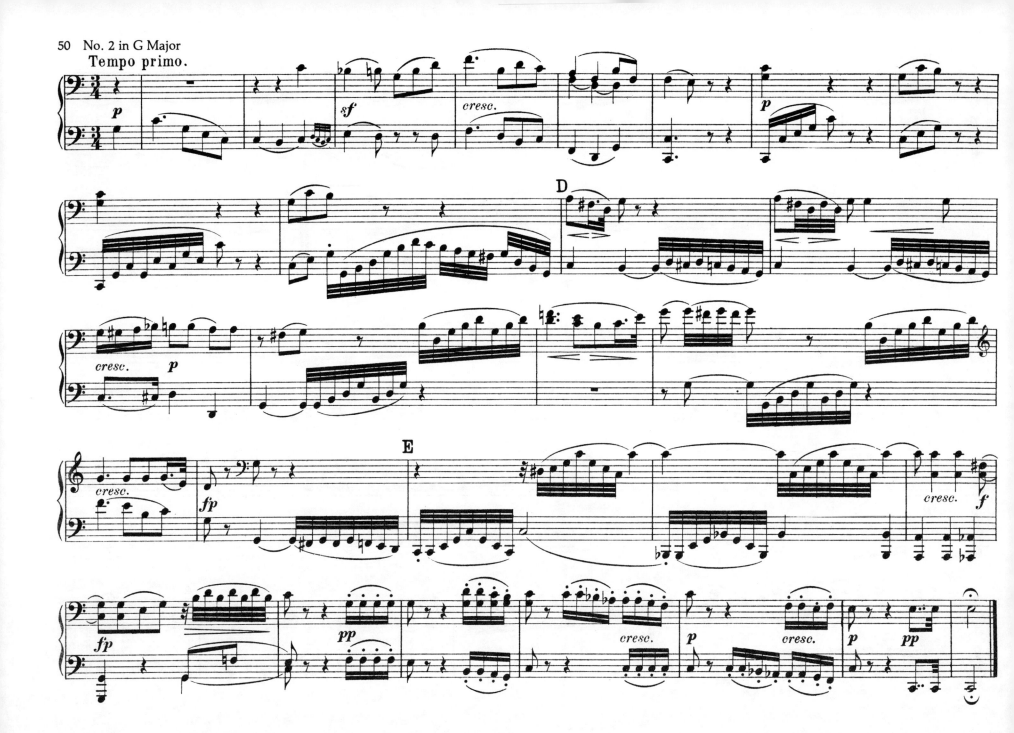

Tempo primo.

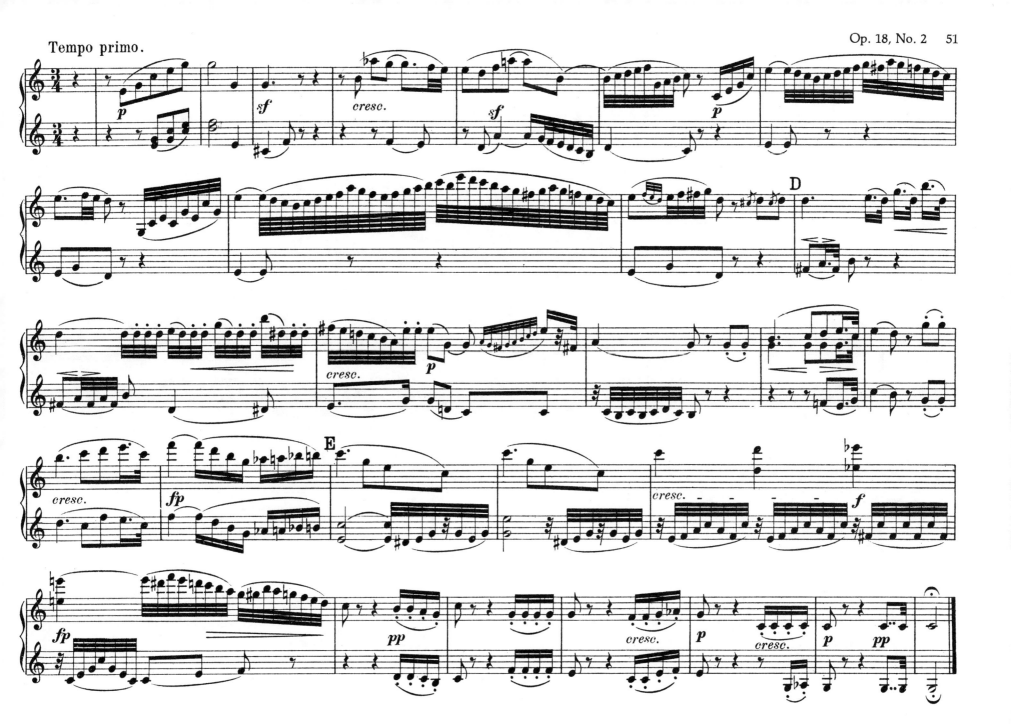

Scherzo.
Allegro.

Scherzo.
Allegro.

Trio.

Scherzo Da Capo.

Scherzo Da Capo.

Allegro molto, quasi Presto.

Allegro molto, quasi Presto.

No. 3 in D Major, Op. 18, No. 3

No. 3 in D Major, Op. 18, No. 3

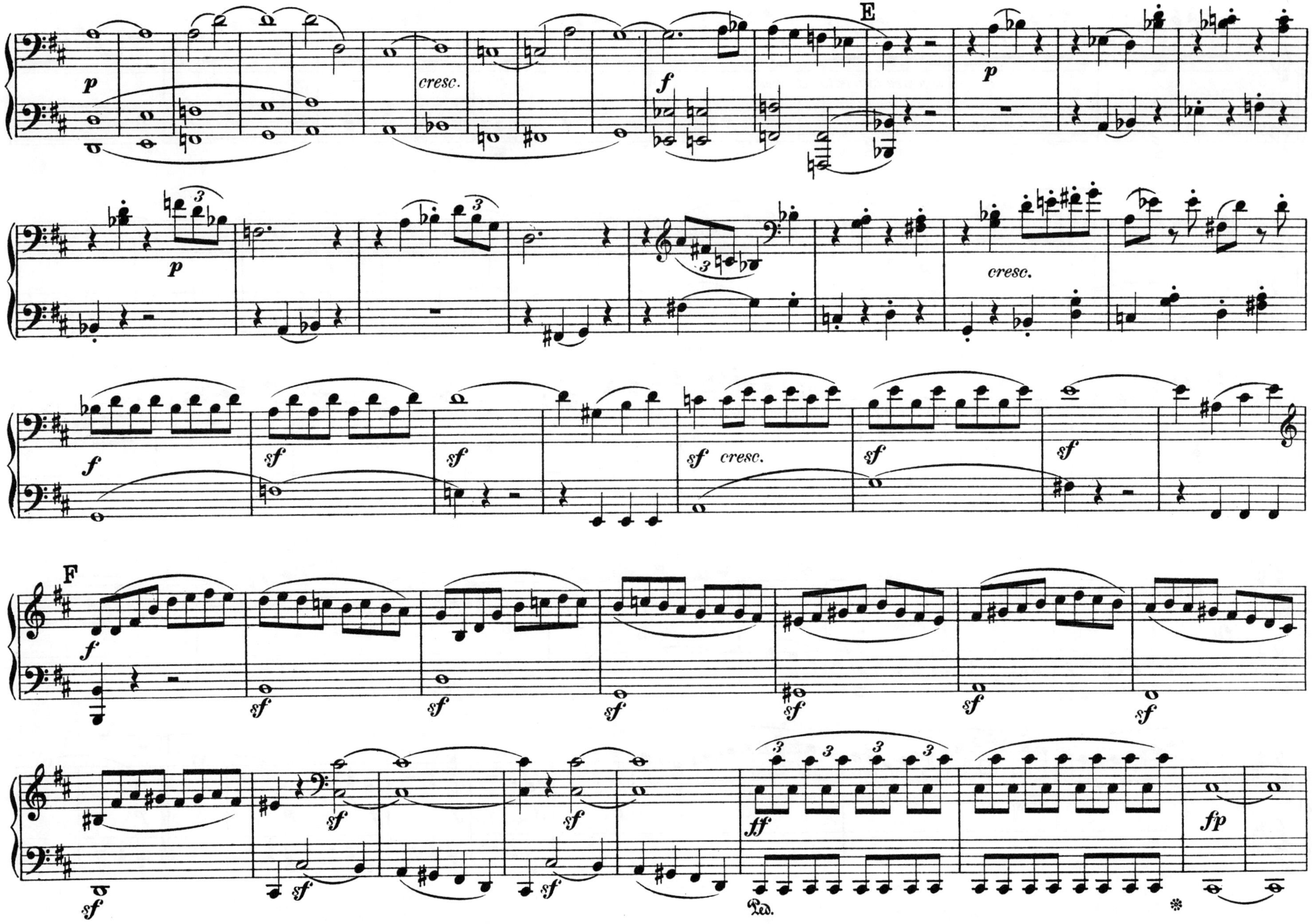
E
p
cresc.
f
F
sf
ff
fp

Andante con moto.

Presto.

No. 4 in C Minor, Op. 18, No. 4

No. 4 in C Minor, Op. 18, No. 4

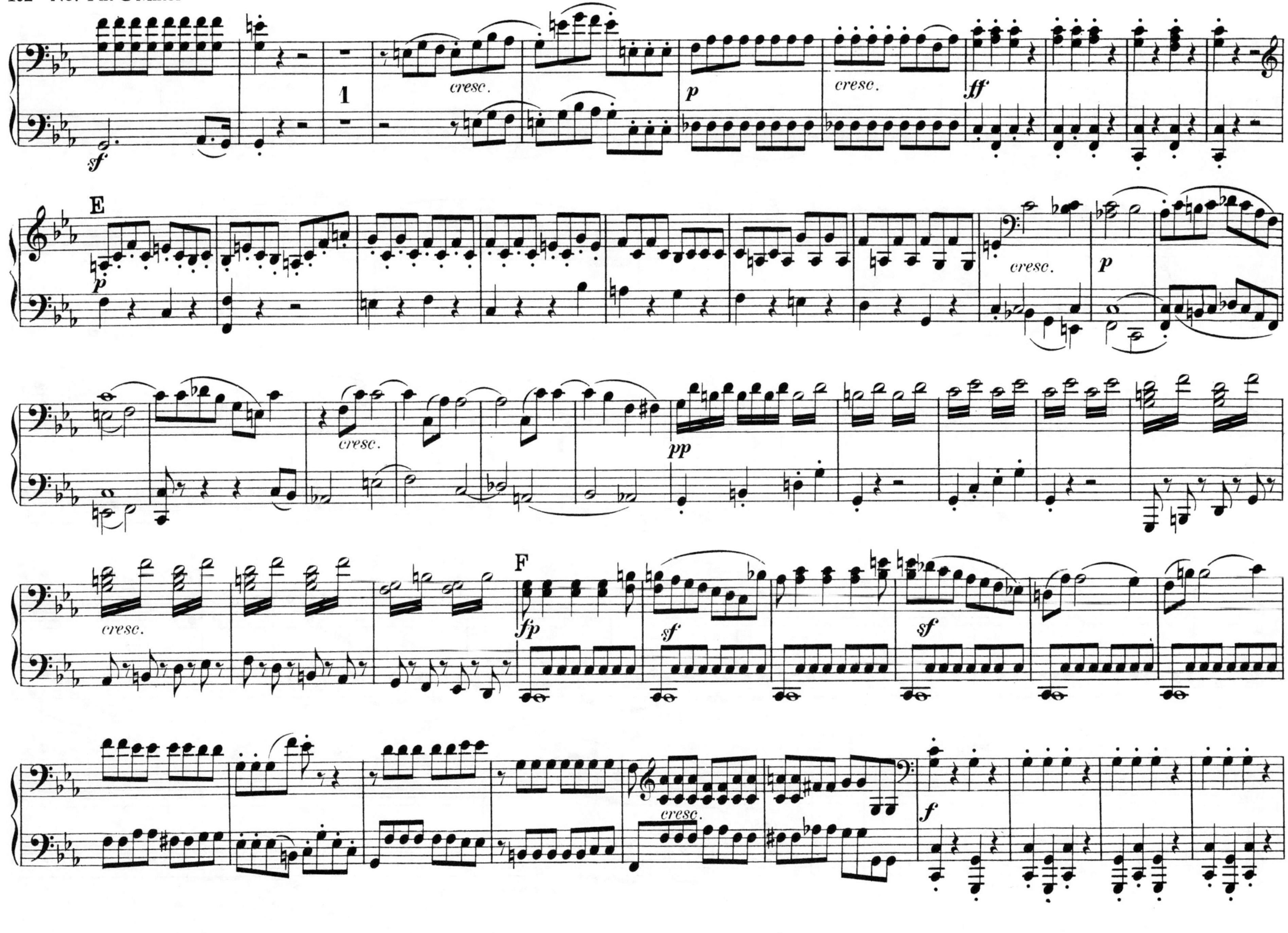
1
cresc.
p
cresc.
ff
E
p
cresc.
p
cresc.
pp
cresc.
F
fp
sf
sf
cresc.
f

Andante scherzoso, quasi Allegretto.

Andante scherzoso, quasi Allegretto.

7769

114 **Menuetto.**

Allegretto.

Trio.

Men. D. Capo.

Men. D. Capo.

Allegro.

No. 5 in A Major, Op. 18, No. 5

No. 5 in A Major, Op. 18, No. 5

136

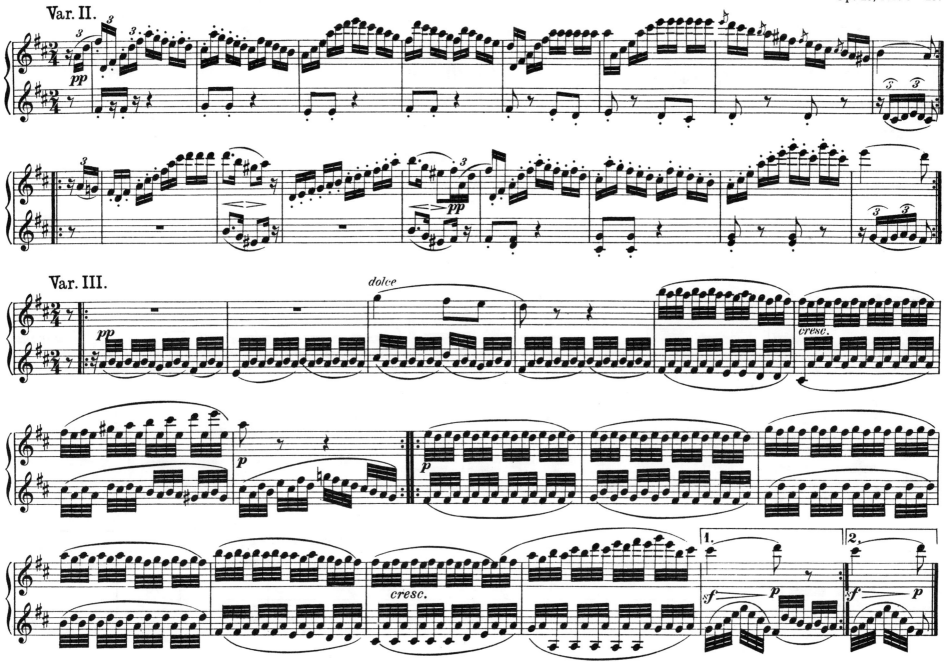

Var. IV.

Var. V.

No. 6 in B-flat Major, Op. 18, No. 6

No. 6 in B-flat Major, Op. 18, No. 6

Adagio, ma non troppo.

Adagio, ma non troppo.

Scherzo.
Allegro.

Scherzo.
Allegro.

Trio.

La Malinconia.
Adagio.
Questo pezzo si deve trattare colla più gran delicatezza.

Allegretto, quasi Allegro.

No. 7 in F Major, Op. 59, No. 1

No. 7 in F Major, Op. 59, No. 1

Allegretto vivace e sempre scherzando.

Allegretto vivace e sempre scherzando.

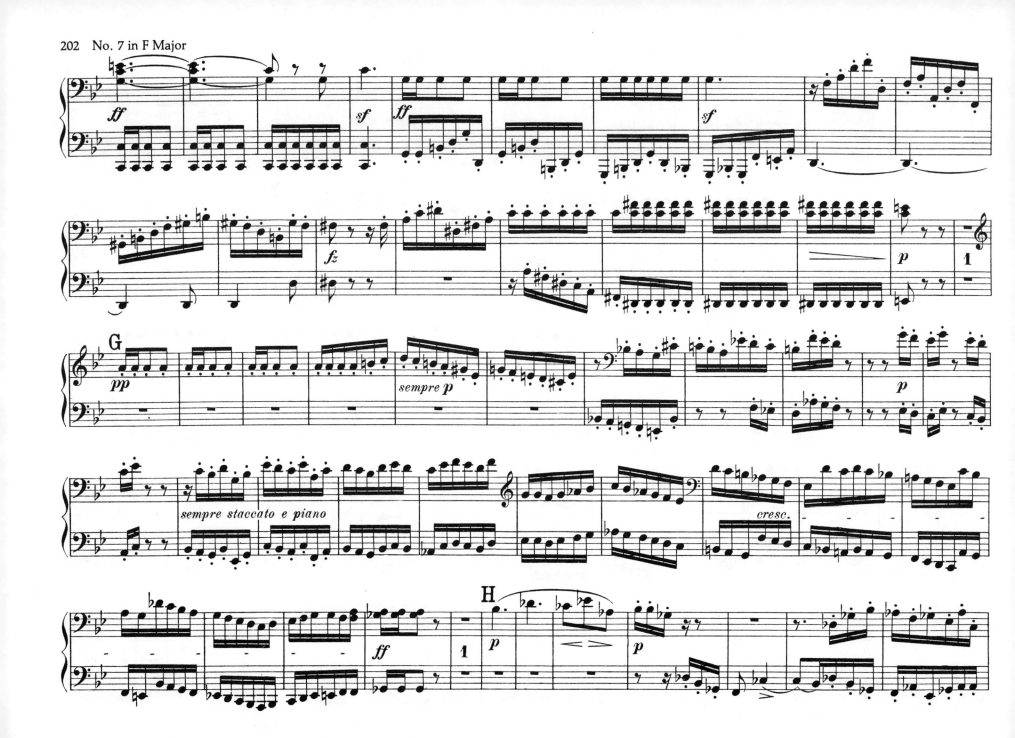

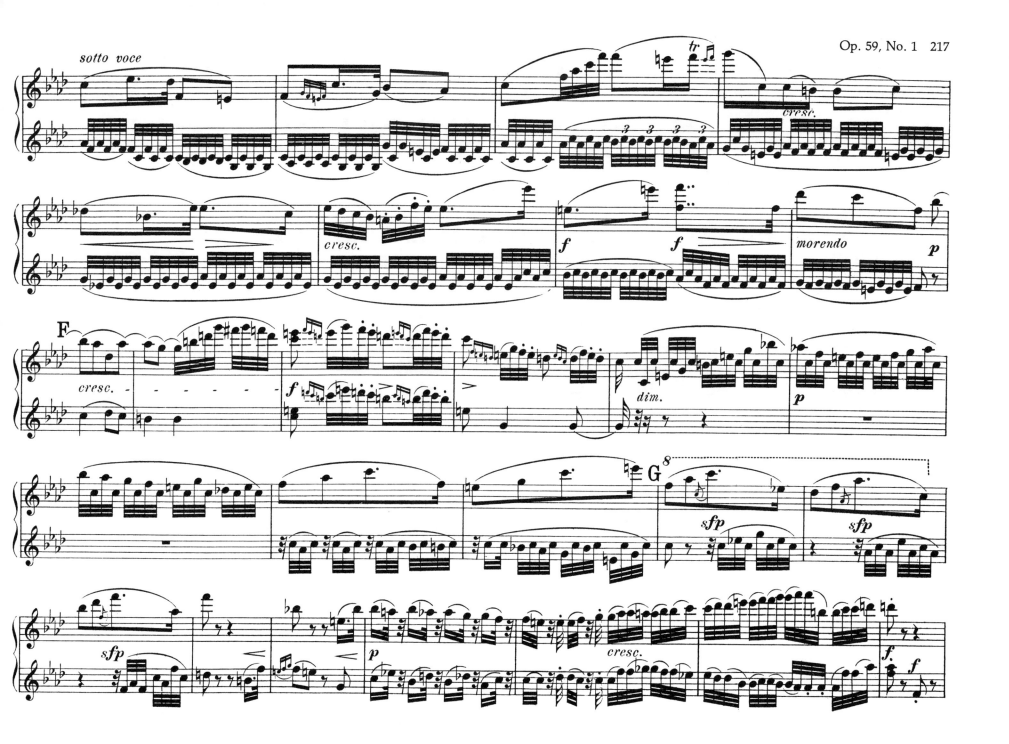

p
dim.
N
pp
ff
sf
poco rit.
pp
a tempo
cresc.
O
f
p
cresc.
f
ff
dim.
p dim.
pp
1
p
cresc.
f
p

No. 8 in E Minor, Op. 59, No. 2

No. 8 in E Minor, Op. 59, No. 2

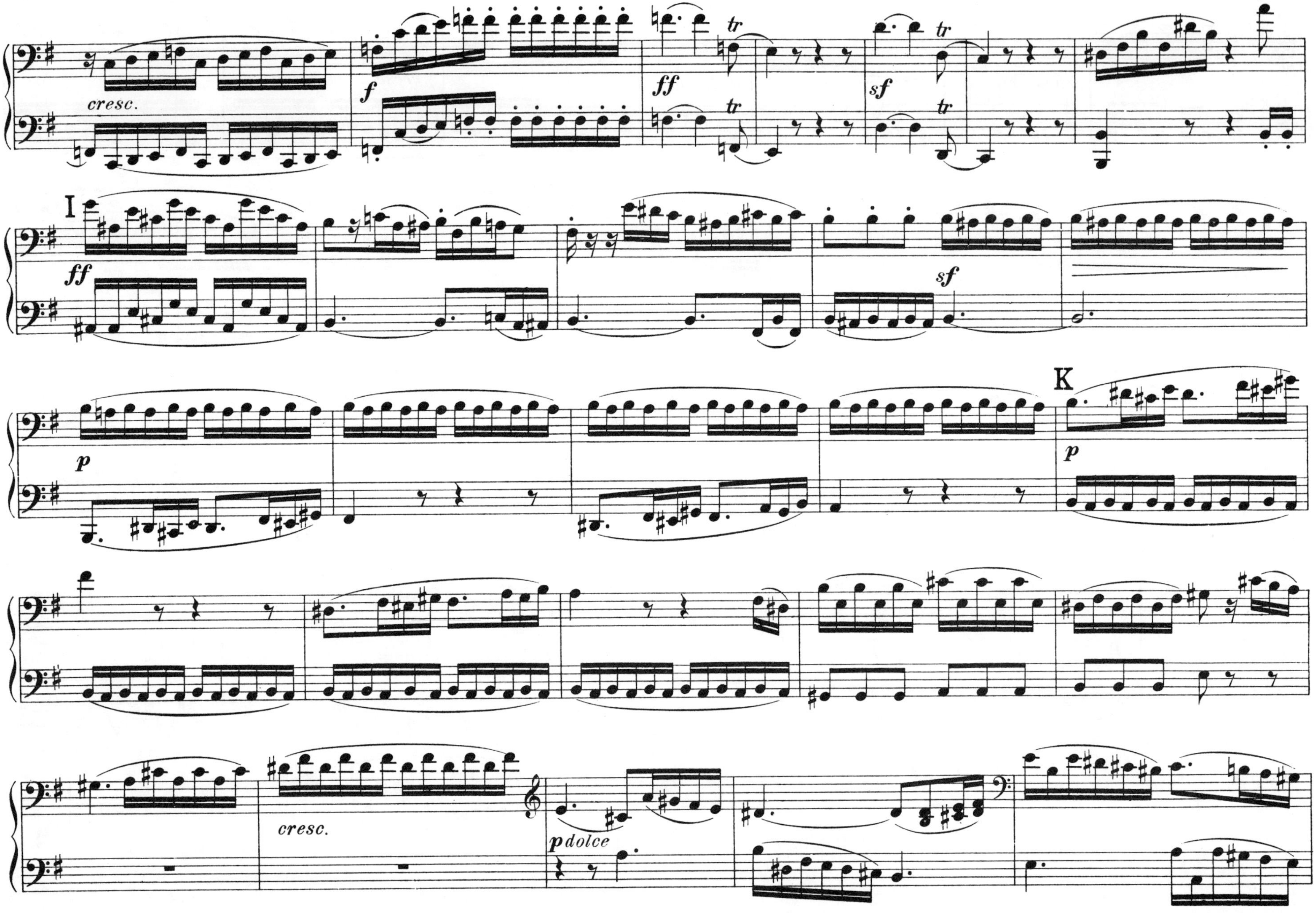
cresc.
f
ff
tr
sf
I
K
p
p dolce

Molto Adagio.

Si tratta questo pezzo con molto di sentimento.

Molto Adagio.

Si tratta questo pezzo con molto di sentimento.

Allegretto.

Da Capo il minore ma senza replica, ed allora ancora una volta il
Trio, e dopo di nuovo da Capo il minore senza replica.

Da Capo il minore ma senza replica, ed allora ancora una volta
il Trio, e dopo di nuovo da Capo il minore senza replica.

Finale.
Presto.

Finale.
Presto.

No. 9 in C Major, Op. 59, No. 3

No. 9 in C Major, Op. 59, No. 3

Andante con moto quasi Allegretto.

Andante con moto quasi Allegretto.

Menuetto.

Menuetto.

296